This

belongs to...

First published in this format in 2003 by
The Medici Society Ltd
Grafton House, Hyde Estate Road, London NW9 6JZ

Copyright © The Medici Society Ltd 2003 / 1925

First published in 1925 by The Medici Society Ltd
1 3 5 7 9 10 8 6 4 2

The rights of Margaret Tarrant and Marion St John Webb to be identified
as the Illustrator and Author of this work have been asserted by them in
accordance with the Copyright, Design and Patents Act 1988.

A catalogue record for this book is available from the British Library.

ISBN 0 85503 255 3

Margaret Tarrant's original artworks have been rescanned for this re-designed edition.

Designed by Tony Potter Publishing Ltd

Printed in Singapore

The
Insect Fairies

Contents

Before the Party Ends

The party is beginning
Down in Brambleberry Wood,
And everyone has brought a friend.
It's always understood
That every little insect
Can invite a fairy friend,
To come along and dance a while,
And play at "Let's pretend."

The fairies like pretending
They've forgotten how to fly;
And when the insects show them how,
They flap their wings and try.
They make believe they cannot,
Then laugh and dance and shout,
And climb upon the insects' backs,
And ride all round about.

The dragonfly's pretending
Is the best of all, you know.
He'll pretend he's an aeroplane,
And swiftly to and fro
He'll take the little fairies,
And he'll skim across the stream.
He knows that is the surest way
To make a fairy scream!

The party is beginning,
And the lanes are all astir,
With tiny feet a-pattering,
And tiny wings a-whirr,
As all the little insects,
And their little fairy friends,
Go down the path to the wood
Before the party ends.

The Caterpillar's Song

I'm glad you've called to see me,
    But I'm just going out.
Shall we go along together?
I'll show you round about.
I can take you to a party
In Brambleberry Wood.
You'll see lots of fairies dancing there,
And the food is always good!

It's getting dark and misty.
I'll ask my little lamp
To light herself, and guide us,
The evening's cold and damp.
My lamp's this tiny glow-worm
As bright as she can be.
Ah, now she's put her light on
That helps us all to see!

If you will wait a moment
I'll get my cosy hat,
And put my endless shoes on;
They're piled up on the mat.
Oh dear! It's very trying
To have so many feet.
If only half of them were hands,
It would be such a treat!

Now, what else is there to take?
Ah yes, of course! My sunshade
My bag, and purse, and thimble,
My bucket and my spade.
I always take them with me
Wherever I may go.
I might be glad I'd brought them all.
Well, you never know.

I'll also take my scissors,
And a bottle full of ink.
A blanket and a cushion,
And a big notebook, I think.
I always take a lampshade
To carry in my arms.
And I really mustn't leave behind
My lucky little charms.

My lucky charms, this locket,
And a fairy in my pocket!

Now come along, I'm ready.
I can't carry any more.
Perhaps you'll bring along the clock?
And oh! please close the door!

Telling the Bees

The fairies of the hill-top
　　Went flying down the dale,
To grow a little garden there,
All sheltered from the gale.
But just before they started
The wisest one cried, "Please,
One of us must fly quickly
To go and tell the bees.

You know what happens if we don't.
The bees are very funny.
They get annoyed and fly away,
And leave us with no honey.
Then everything goes wrong with us,
And all our luck will fail."
So first the fairies told the bees,
And then went down the dale.

And so, of course, their garden grew,
With flowers and fruits and trees.
And they had honey every day,
Because they told the bees.

The fairies of the lowlands
Went flying up the hill,
To do a little work there,
And turn a fairy mill.
They needed flour for baking
A special party cake.
And every fairy worked
Until their arms did ache.

They didn't tell the bees.
"Whatever does it matter?
We don't believe in telling them,
That's just silly chatter."
But everything went wrong from then.
They had a dreadful day.
Because they hadn't told the bees
Their flour came out all grey!

And when they went to have their tea,
At five o'clock that day,
There wasn't any honey,
For the bees had flown away!

A Tap at the Window

A wasp came tap, tap, tapping one day
　　At the window pane.
And inside the room he heard a voice say
"It must be the fairies again!"
Then the window was opened out wide,
So the wasp, much delighted, went flying
　inside.

"They'll be glad when they see it is me
For such a very fine wasp I am!"
And seeing the table was set out for tea,
Went flying down and sat in the jam.
"Oh, look! It's a horrid old wasp!" a voice
  cried,
And they shoo'd him, then chased him
  outside.

A fairy came tap, tap, tapping one day
At the window pane.
And inside the room she heard a voice say
"It must be that wasp back again!"
The window was shut with a slam and a
  shout,
Then it was locked, and the fairy shut out!

So if there's a tap on your window, I pray,
Make sure it's no fairy you're sending
 away!

I'd like to be a Fairy

I'd like to be a fairy
    When the winter time is here,
And butterflies have gone to sleep,
And Christmas trees appear;
And snow lies softly glistening,
As Holly Fairies sing.
I'd like to be a fairy then,
And wear a silver ring.
Silver like the moonlit rain,
And frost upon the window-pane.

I'd like to be a fairy
When winter time is past,
And tiny little primroses
Are peeping through at last;
And early yellow butterflies
Announce that it is spring.
I'd like to be a fairy then,
And wear a golden ring .
Golden like the sunny skies,
And daffodils, and butterflies.

Fly Away Home

Mrs Ladybird one day set out
To travel up to town,
She flew a bit, and then walked a bit,
Then in a hedge sat down.
She thought she'd rest a little while,
But she'd not been there too long,
When suddenly a goblin's voice
Began to sing this song:

> "Ladybird, ladybird,
> Fly away home.
> Your house is on fire,
> Your children have flown!"

But Mrs. Ladybird she sat still.
And listened to the goblin sing,
Then took a notice from her bag,
And stuck it on her wing.

And so when the teasing goblin
From the hedge did raise his head,
He found Mrs Ladybird still there,
And on her wing he read:
    "Three hundred scares I've had.
    Three hundred times I've been
    Away back home to stop the fire,
    The fire I've never seen!
    I always found my house quite safe,
    And locked, my little door.
    My children are all grown now,
    I'll go back home no more!"

Margaret Winifred Tarrant (1888 - 1959)

'Every time a child says, " I don't believe in fairies," ' warned Peter Pan, 'there is a little fairy somewhere that falls down dead.' By her paintings Margaret Tarrant did as much to encourage children's belief in fairies as J M Barrie did by his writings. Born in London in 1888, the only child of artist Percy Tarrant and his wife Sarah, Margaret excelled at art from an early age, and she was only 19 when she received her first, very prestigious, commission, from J M Dent & Sons: to illustrate Charles Kingsley's much-loved children's classic, *The Water Babies*, which was first published in 1863.

Her delicate, charming pictures matched the spirit of the story perfectly and earned her a string of new commissions: *Nursery Rhymes* (1914 and 1923), *Alice in Wonderland* (1916) and

Hans Andersen's Fairy Tales (1917) for Ward Lock & Co., plus postcards for Oxford University Press.

Margaret Tarrant illustrated some 20 books for George G. Harrap & Co. between 1915 and 1929, but an even more important publishing relationship began in 1920, when she completed her first pieces for The Medici Society. This was to prove a long and fruitful connection, resulting in most of her best-known work. In the 1920s, for example, she illustrated this highly successful series of fairy books for the company, written by the poet and author Marion St John Webb. Her picture of Peter's Friends, inspired by J M Barrie's *Peter Pan* stories and the statue in Kensington Gardens, proved so popular when it appeared in 1921 that it had to be reproduced many times.

Peter's Friends

The dusk of the nineteenth and dawn of the twentieth centuries were magical times for fairy lovers. Fascination with fairy lore was widespread, reaching unprecedented heights in 1922 when Sir Arthur Conan Doyle published *The Coming of the Fairies*, containing 'photographs' of fairies taken by two young girls in a Yorkshire village, which were later proved to be hoaxes. The story was actually a fascinating deception, which was believed by many reputable people. The mystery was not solved until towards the end of the twentieth century, when the girls involved, now elderly ladies, explained what had really happened.

In 1922, Margaret Tarrant's *Do You Believe in Fairies?* showed two children encircled by a ring of fairies, which caught the public excitement already created by Sir Arthur Conan Doyle's book.

This interest was mirrored in an outpouring of art and literature. Children's books cultivated belief in fairies: they were used in religious teaching, magazines were devoted to them, and captivating new works appeared, most notably J M Barrie's *Peter Pan* and *Peter Pan in Kensington Gardens*. Rudyard Kipling wrote *Rewards and Fairies* and even Beatrix Potter embraced the subject in *The Fairy Caravan*.

Artists revelled in the opportunity to portray imaginary worlds. Arthur Rackham, the most fashionable illustrator of his day, depicted a sinister fantasy landscape, peopled by spiky goblins, fairies and mice amid gnarled trees with gnomelike faces. In contrast, Honor Appleton, Maud Tindal Atkinson and Mabel Lucie Atwell offered gentler, comforting images recalling Kate Greenaway's illustrations of apple-cheeked children.

Margaret Tarrant was one of those most associated with the depiction of fairies in the 1920s and 1930s, together with her friend and sketching partner, Cicely Mary Barker (1895 - 1973). Both began to use Art Nouveau and Arts and Crafts

elements in their work, and in Tarrant's paintings a breathtaking attention to detail - diaphanous wings with the intricate tracery of a dragonfly's wings - is a testament to the reality of fairies, imaginary or otherwise.

During her life Margaret Tarrant tackled a wide range of subjects and won special acclaim for those, such as *All Things Wise and Wonderful*, with a religious theme. But her forte was fairies, for in her evocation of these ethereal figures she could express her love for children, wild flowers and dance, of all that was beautiful and pure.

She would sketch meticulously from life to capture the likeness of a child or plant, then compose her pictures by arranging the subjects in imaginary settings, infusing them with a distinctive otherworldly quality.

Margaret Tarrant's fairies have a unique fluidity and balletic grace that expressed her delight in the free-flowing dance invented by Isadora Duncan. She was very much a free spirit herself, flying along the country lanes around her home in Surrey on an ancient bicycle, leaping off impulsively to sketch a flower or help a toddler to paint. She never married, but she attracted many friends by her generosity, energy and zest for life. Perhaps it was this childlike enthusiasm and innocence, combined with a special kind of imagination, that gave her a natural affinity with fairies.

The Lily Pool

Much missed when she died in 1959, Margaret Tarrant left a lasting legacy in charming pictures that seem as fresh today as the day they were painted, and still enchant new generations with their glimpses into a secret fairy world.

The new edition

There are 12 beautiful fairy books by Margaret Tarrant, originally published between 1923 - 1928. The re-designed edition is now available to collect as a set, with modern scanning methods used to bring out the exquisite detail of the original paintings and drawings.

WATER FAIRIES — WATER FAIRIES

TWILIGHT FAIRIES — TWILIGHT FAIRIES

WEATHER FAIRIES — WEATHER FAIRIES

ORCHARD FAIRIES — ORCHARD FAIRIES

FRUIT FAIRIES — WILD FRUIT FAIRIES

INSECT FAIRIES — INSECT FAIRIES

HOUSE FAIRIES — HOUSE FAIRIES

FOREST FAIRIES — FOREST FAIRIES

SEED FAIRIES — SEED FAIRIES

SEASHORE FAIRIES — SEASHORE FAIRIES

FLOWER FAIRIES — FLOWER FAIRIES

HEATH FAIRIES — HEATH FAIRIES

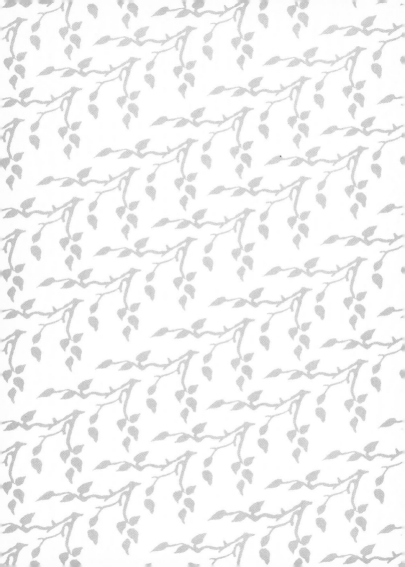